398.2
Spe
c.1

Spellman, John W
The beautiful blue
jay and other tales of
India

Date Due

MACD C 1 01 '77			
MONTA 12. 2498.			
MONTA J 9 / 13 79			
BIG S			
3-1966	10 8 '84		

Twenty-five fascinating tales of a faraway land, an entirely different collection from other Indian stories. You will be interested in the similarities to the familiar English tales but these have a flavor all their own. Beautifully illustrated to capture the mood of fantasy.

The Beautiful Blue Jay
And Other Tales of India

The Beautiful Blue Jay
And Other Tales of India

Collected and Edited
by John W. Spellman

Illustrated by Jerry Pinkney

Little, Brown and Company
BOSTON   TORONTO

Published simultaneously in Canada
by Little, Brown & Company (Canada) Limited

PRINTED IN THE UNITED STATES OF AMERICA

For Suzanne Bhāratī
and John Gilligan

INTRODUCTION

THESE TALES from Children's India have been gathered from all over India. They differ from previous collections in a number of ways. Most of them have never, as far as I know, appeared in print before. They are not based on the treasuries of classical Indian stories such as the Mahābhārata, Pañchatantra or Jātakas. These are the tales that mothers actually tell their children in India today. Many of them are based on themes which are universal in the world of children's literature; yet they show the distinctiveness of India within that universality. They illustrate the intermingling of religious and national cultures. They reflect the humor, the struggles, the concerns and the behavior of the common folk of India. These stories are, in a sense, a document of Indian life. Amidst the fabulous and strange occurrences, this fact stands out.

One of the overriding themes in these stories is that of hunger for food. This is not because I selected tales with this theme but because it is one of the harsh realities of the life of millions in India. They pit their humor and wit against it, and in the stories, at least, they are successful. Those who think of India as a land resigned to fate will not find that belief supported here.

The rich, the braggart, the unkind, the stepmother or mother-in-law are outwitted in children's tales the world over. The simpleton is always wiser than we thought, and it always pays to be kind and helpful to a stranger—especially should you meet him on the road or at your house. Notice that the stranger is not usually an evil person. The aged and poor shoemaker had his entire life changed for the better when he took in a stranger, as did Gopal when he befriended one along the road.

The highest class of India — the Brahmans — appear both as detached saints and scheming scoundrels. The contrast between Yatnakant, who refuses all wealth, and the Panditji, who cannot resist stealing, in his own way, the fragrant guava fruits from the poor but shrewd farmer, gives us some insight into the Brahman's life.

The story of the crow and the sparrow is a favorite of younger children and like other children's tales has a number of versions. The one here is based on the Konkani with some embroidering from other versions. The popularity of the story of the origin of Mother's Day may in part be related to the fact that in Maharashtra the children receive special sweets on that day. Few stories illustrate better than "One More Child" how precious children are. The teller of this story remarked that after hearing her mother tell this tale she and her brothers and sisters were always careful not to waste food. She remembered that when Mother India was even poorer than she is today, another child was still a blessing.

With the advent of British rule and English education in India, more and more Indian children, especially those of the upper classes, were told English fairy tales, and some of them never heard the stories that grew from their own country. Today some of them are parents, and perhaps from this book they may be able to transmit better a heritage that they themselves missed.

It is well that children in other lands know of the kinship and bonds that they have with children the world over — in this case with Indian children. The thing all people have most in common is that they are human beings and not alien geographical entities.

For those of us who are older, there is hopefully still the child in us which needs to be re-affirmed from time to time. And we need once more to look into the world of beauty, wonder and simplicity that we once shared. I hope this book will help do that for you.

Obviously this collection makes no pretense at being exhaustive. Many of the tales of children in India are, in fact, from the classical literature; still others are based on local events or religious literature. Perhaps someday we may have a complete collection of these. But in this book we are limited to a slice of the oral tales of India today.

These stories are the products of many minds. I would like to thank some of those who contributed stories — Mrs. G. S. Bhat, Margaret R. Bhatty, T. Chandrashekaran, Mrs. T. A. D'Souza, J. N. Mukherjee, Mrs. A. K. Rao, Rosemary Ridewood, Ram Nandan Sahat, Samananda, S. S. Guha Sircar, Pratima Srivastava, Mrs. B. S. Tarapore, P. G. Thakar. Special mention must be made of Mr. T. Chandrashekaran, who sent many delightful stories and was a source of constant enthusiasm for this research. To M. M. Spellman I owe much gratitude for assistance given over several years.

J.W.S.

Seattle, Washington

CONTENTS

Contents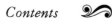

❧

*The Beautiful Blue Jay
And Other Tales of India*

❧

THE BEAUTIFUL BLUE JAY

THERE IS a bird in India called the blue jay. It is a beautiful bird, but it has a very ugly voice. This was not always so. Here is the story of how the jay got its blue feathers but lost its beautiful voice.

Many, many years ago, the jay was a small brown bird. He had no lovely blue feathers, but he sang more sweetly than any other bird in India. Every morning when the sun came up, the little jay would be the first bird to sing, and people opened their eyes and said: "It is time to get up. Listen to the little jay. How beautifully he sings."

The lovely Princess Lakshmi heard the little bird singing in her garden, and she said, "How I wish I could sing like the jay. Then Prince Rama might marry me."

Prince Rama was a very handsome young man and Princess Lakshmi loved him very much. Every morning she sat at her window in order to watch him going down the road on his fine black horse. But the prince never looked at her. He did not look because he could not; Prince Rama was blind. And so he did

3

not know that the Princess was as beautiful as a lotus flower; he only knew that she had an ugly voice. Poor, unhappy Lakshmi. When she tried to sing, everyone laughed. "Your voice sounds like an old crow's," her mother said. "Don't try to sing, Lakshmi. Your face is very beautiful but your voice certainly is not."

"But Prince Rama can't see my face," thought Lakshmi, and sadly she went out into the garden. The little jay was singing his sweet song, and the Princess listened, filled with unhappiness. "O little brown bird," she said at last. "Give me your voice. Please give me your lovely voice."

The jay stopped singing and looked at her with his shining eyes. Was it true? Was this lovely Princess asking him for his voice? She looked so unhappy, too.

"Beautiful Princess Lakshmi," said the jay, "why do you ask me for my voice?"

"Because I love Prince Rama," answered Lakshmi, "and he is blind. He doesn't care for me because he can hear only my ugly voice." And the unhappy Princess started to cry.

"Don't cry. Please don't cry," pleaded the jay. "I will give you my voice."

Princess Lakshmi stopped crying and looked at the little brown bird. "Are you serious?" she asked. "How could you possibly give me your voice?"

"Tonight is the night of the full moon," replied the jay. "At exactly twelve o'clock, go to the lotus pool at the bottom of your garden. You will see one lotus in the pool. Take it in your hand and say:

> *Lotus, lovely lotus flower,*
> *In this quiet midnight hour,*

Make my voice sing through the days
As sweetly as the little jay's.

Lakshmi looked towards the lotus pool at the bottom of the garden and then turned to thank the little bird. But the jay had flown away, without even waiting for her thanks.

That night, five minutes before twelve o'clock, Princess Lakshmi jumped up from her bed and went to the window. The big yellow moon was shining brightly but the night was cold, so she took a blue and gold Benaras scarf and put it over her head. Then she stepped quietly from her house and walked down to the lotus pool. Just as the jay predicted she saw one lotus shining in the moonlight. She went down on her knees beside it, took the flower in her hands, and said:

Lotus, lovely lotus flower,
In this quiet midnight hour,
Make my voice sing through the days
As sweetly as the little jay's.

At once Lakshmi knew that she could sing. Still on her knees beside the pool, she sang a lovely birdlike song more beautiful than any other song she had ever heard. Lakshmi cried with happiness.

"O little brown jay, where are you?" she said. "Thank you, thank you a hundred times." She heard an ugly little voice beside her saying: "I am glad to make you happy, beautiful princess."

Lakshmi looked around and then she saw the little brown jay. His black eyes were shining, but his body was shivering with cold. "I'm not usually out at night," he said, "but I did

so want to hear you sing." His voice was harsh and noisy.

"O little jay," cried Lakshmi, "you are very cold. Here, I'll give you my scarf." She took the beautiful blue and gold Benaras scarf from her head and wrapped it carefully around the trembling jay. "Now you look very beautiful," she said. "I wish that you could always be as beautiful as this."

And all at once the jay's feathers took on the shining colors of the scarf. He was a drab brown jay no more; now he was a beautiful blue jay. Lakshmi looked down and saw that she still had the lotus flower in her hand. That was why her second wish had also come true.

The jay flew off, talking noisily in his ugly voice, and Lakshmi went back to bed, singing quietly to herself.

Six months later, there was great joy and gladness in the town. Princess Lakshmi, "the Princess with the beautiful voice," was married to Prince Rama. Everyone was happy, but no one was happier than the little blue jay as he flew through the Prince's garden, his beautiful new feathers shining in the morning sun.

THE KING AND THE SHOEMAKER

ONCE upon a time long ago there was a shoemaker. He made very good shoes, but he was growing old and his eyes were weak. He worked slowly because he could not see very well.

People said, "We will go to another shoemaker. We want our shoes to be made quickly, and we cannot wait so long. Your work is too slow."

So the poor old shoemaker had no money to buy new leather. He had no sons to look after him and he lived all alone. It was not long before he became tired and ill because he did not have enough food to eat.

Now, the shoemaker had one beautiful piece of leather which he had bought many years before. It was a fine soft piece of red leather. He had never made it into shoes because he liked it very much and wanted to keep it with him always. But now he took it out of his cupboard and looked at it again.

"I will make this leather into a beautiful pair of shoes," he said. "It cost a lot of money so the shoes will be expensive. Perhaps someone will pay me thirty *rupees* for them, and I can buy food and more leather with the money."

So the shoemaker got out his tools and made a pair of red shoes. He worked slowly and carefully, and they were the most beautiful shoes he had ever made. He displayed them in his shop and waited for someone to come and buy them.

The next day a man came into the shop. "What is the price of those red shoes?" he asked.

"Thirty rupees," said the man.

"The young shoemaker across the street can make me a pair of shoes for fifteen rupees."

"But this is very good leather," explained the old shoemaker. "And I have made the shoes very carefully. You will be able to wear them for many years."

"I like to buy a new pair of shoes every year," said the man. "And I do not want to pay thirty rupees for them."

He walked out of the shop.

The same thing happened again and again. People saw the beautiful red shoes in the shop, but they all said they would not pay thirty rupees for one pair of shoes. They all went to the young shoemaker who lived across the street. The poor old shoemaker was very unhappy.

One evening he was sitting sadly in his house. He had spent his last two *annas* and had bought himself a cup of coffee and a loaf of bread.

"Tomorrow I shall have no food," he thought. "What is to become of me?"

It was raining outside and a cold wind was blowing. Suddenly the shoemaker heard a knock on his door. He got up and opened the door. A poor beggar stood shivering outside.

"Please, will you give me an anna?" asked the beggar. "I am cold and wet, and I have had no food today."

"I, too, have no money and no food," said the old shoemaker. "I have just spent my last two annas. But come in anyway and dry yourself beside my fire. You can sleep here tonight."

The beggar came inside and sat beside the fire. He had no shoes, and his feet were sore where the stones had cut them as he walked along the roads.

"Why have you no money, old man?" he asked.

"I am too old," the shoemaker replied. "I cannot work quickly, and everyone buys shoes from the young shoemaker who lives across the street."

The beggar picked up the new red shoes and looked at them. "These are very beautiful shoes," he said. "Why do you not sell these?"

"No one will buy them," said the shoemaker. "They say the shoes are too expensive."

"I should like a pair of shoes like that," said the beggar sadly. "My feet are sore and bleeding. But, of course, I have no money at all."

"Take the red shoes," the shoemaker said. "No one will buy them, and perhaps they will bring you good luck."

Then the shoemaker went to bed and left the beggar sitting by the fire.

When the old man woke up next morning the beggar had gone. He had taken the new red shoes with him. The shoemaker lighted his fire and heated a cup of water to drink. He had nothing to eat. All morning he sat beside the fire, wondering what could have happened to the beggar.

At one o'clock he heard a knock on his door. He went to open it and was very surprised to see a finely dressed servant standing outside. The servant was holding a brass food carrier. "I have brought your food," he said.

"My food!" cried the shoemaker. "I don't understand. I think there must be some mistake."

The servant smiled. "There is no mistake," he said. "Last night you gave my master a pair of shoes, and he wants to repay you."

"But I gave the shoes to a beggar," said the puzzled shoemaker. "Who is your master?"

"My master is the Maharajah," said the servant. "This village belongs to him. Sometimes he gets tired of living in his palace, and he dresses like a beggar and walks through the villages. In this way he can find out whether the people are happy. Last night you thought he was a poor beggar and you gave him the only thing you had. You gave him your beautiful red shoes. Today my master sends you food, and he says he will take care of you all your life."

So the shoemaker was happy and well fed in his old age. The Maharajah never forgot him, and sometimes he would come to the village and talk to the old man. And whenever he came, the Maharajah wore the beautiful red shoes.

THE CROW AND THE SPARROW

ONCE upon a time there was a crow and a sparrow. The crow picked up little twigs, sticks, straw and other things from dirty places and built his nest upon a tree. But the sparrow searched for strands of cotton, flax and silk, and built her nest neatly in a nice niche.

One day there was a terrible storm and down came the crow's nest. Poor fellow. He was cold, drenched and shivering. While he stood sadly looking at his loss, he thought of taking shelter under the roof of his neighbor, the sparrow.

Quietly and hopefully he approached the sparrow's house and gently tapped on the door. "Gupchakka, Gupchakka (Sister Sparrow, Sister Sparrow). Won't you please open the door?"

"Wait awhile," replied the sparrow. "I am bathing the babies."

Again the crow tapped on the door. "Gupchakka, won't you open the door?"

"Wait a bit," said the sparrow. "I'm rubbing down the babies with the towel."

The crow again cried, "Gupchakka, Gupchakka. Please open the door."

"Hold on," the sparrow said. "I'm burning incense to dry the babies."

"Gupchakka, Gupchakka. Please open the door."

"Just a minute, I'm dressing the babies."

"Gupchakka, Gupchakka. Pray open the door."

"Please wait. I'm giving them milk."

"Gupchakka, Gupchakka. Won't you open the door?"

"Not until I finish powdering them."

"Gupchakka, Gupchakka. Please open the door."

"Wait, I am putting them to sleep."

In this way she kept on giving one excuse or another. Still the crow would not go away.

Again the crow cried, "Gupchakka, Gupchakka. Please open the door."

At last, utterly exasperated, she had to open the door and let in the crow.

When he came in he said, "I am dying of cold and hunger, without any shelter. Please do something for me."

"Now," said the sparrow, "where will you sleep? Will the bed do?"

"No, no," said the crow. "Suppose it falls."

"Will the cupboard do?"

"No, no, suppose that too tumbles down."

"Then will you sleep in the cradle?" asked Gupchakka.

"Yes," the crow readily replied. "I think that's a good place."

That night when all were asleep, the sparrow heard sounds of "kuttu, kuttu, kuttu."

"Crow, Crow," said the sparrow. "What on earth are you eating at this time of night?"

"Nothing much," the crow replied. "Only a grain an old woman gave me."

The next morning when the sparrow woke up, what did she find? All her little ones were missing. The crow had eaten them up. She was terribly upset and angry. "I'll teach the crow a lesson he'll never forget," she said and thrust a pair of tongs into the fire until they were red-hot. When the crow opened his mouth to say "Caw," she shoved the tongs down his throat. Out burst her little ones from inside, and they all lived happily ever after.

THE LAZY GARDENER
AND THE LITTLE RED MAN

∾

ONCE there was a gardener who was a very lazy man. When his master was in the garden, he worked hard, but as soon as his master went to his office, the gardener sat under a tree and went to sleep. All the flowers died because he gave them no water, and his master was very angry.

"How can I make this lazy man do some work?" said the master.

One day an old woman by the name of Mona came into the garden. She was a very clever old woman who could do many wonderful things. One day the milkman's cow was ill. Mona said some strange words and the cow got better. Another day a fisherman could catch no fish. Mona held his net in her hands and soon it was full of fish.

"I'll make this lazy gardener work harder," she said. She then spoke to the gardener. "Do you want to be a rich man?"

The gardener thought this was a wonderful idea. He would

not have to do any work if he was rich. He did not like work.

"Yes, please," he said to Mona. "I should like to be rich."

The old woman gave him a small black seed.

"Take this seed," she said, "and put it in the ground. It will grow very quickly, and it will make you rich."

So the gardener put the seed in his master's garden and watered it very carefully. The next morning when he came to look at it, it was two feet tall. At the top of the plant there was a pretty red flower.

"Ah," said the gardener. "This is wonderful. But how will it make me rich? Perhaps I must pick the flower and sell it in the market."

As he put out his hand to pick the flower, he heard someone say, "Please don't pick me."

The gardener looked at the flower and saw a very small man inside. The man was dressed in red from his head to his feet. Even his nose was red. And he was only as big as the gardener's finger. The little red man jumped out of the flower and said, "Come on, come on. You have work to do. Hurry, hurry, hurry up."

He made the gardener work very hard. At ten o'clock in the morning all the flowers were watered, but still the gardener had to work. At one o'clock the little red man said, "Now you can have your dinner. But you must start work again at two o'clock."

"Two o'clock?" said the gardener. "I always sleep until five o'clock."

"Not today," said the little red man. "You have work to do."

"I never heard such talk," said the gardener. I shall sleep as long as I like."

But at two o'clock the little red man woke him up and made him start work again.

"Come on, come on. Hurry, hurry, hurry," said the little red man.

The gardener was very angry. What did old Mona mean by her promise?

"That seed will never make me rich," complained the gardener. "It is making me work too hard, and I shall grow thin and die. No man can live if he works so hard."

But the next day the work did not seem so hard. The gardener had the same work to do, but he found he enjoyed doing it. It was really quite pleasant to work in a garden. "Perhaps I shall not die after all," thought the gardener, and he worked very well all day. He even forgot to go and rest. The little red man had to say to him, "You must go and rest now. It is nearly two o'clock. You will be too tired."

The gardener rested until three o'clock, and then he went back to work.

"I must make the paths tidy before my master comes home," he said.

The garden soon looked very beautiful and everyone came to look at it. "What a good gardener you have," they said to the gardener's master.

And Mona was quite right. The gardener's master went away to another country, and the gardener went to work for a Maharajah who made him head gardener of a very large garden. He was paid so much money that he soon became rich.

He never saw the little red man again, but he still worked hard because he found he enjoyed it.

THE PRINCE AND THE DEMON

A CERTAIN KING had seven sons, all of whom he married off on the same day. He then started building a tremendous castle with apartments for all the seven sons and their wives. But as soon as a wall was completed it would be found the next morning all torn down. A *sadhu* (holy man) advised the king that to remove the curse either the eldest son or the youngest daughter-in-law should be sacrificed. Since it would not be possible to replace an eldest son, the youngest daughter-in-law was told that she must be sacrificed the next day.

During the night the young woman and her husband fled as fast as they could away from the king's palace. They came to a thick forest where they found an old woman alone in her little hut. They asked her for shelter.

"You may stay," she replied, "but at your own risk, for there is a demon in this part of the forest who has consumed all the other people of the village. Only I remain and it is coming to eat me tonight."

The prince was not afraid. "I can deal with him," he said.

Do you have a long rope, a pair of tongs and a large millstone?"
The old woman was able to provide him with all these things.
He then collected a handful of pebbles from the nearby stream.

At midnight the shrieking demon came to the cottage. The
prince refused to open the door. The demon was furious and
demanded to know who it was that dared to stand up to him.
"Put out your topknot," he bellowed. "See, I pass mine through
the hole in the door. You see that I am as huge as a giant."
The demon's topknot was long and thick. But the clever prince
passed the end of the thick rope through the hole and kept
passing it yard by yard. The demon said to himself, "A man
with such a tremendous topknot must be very huge indeed!"
And he fled.

The next night hunger drove the demon back to the cottage
door. This time he challenged the prince inside to a pinching

competition. The prince accepted, put out the iron tongs and pinched the demon black and blue.

The next night the demon challenged him to grind his teeth to see who could make the more fearful noise. This time the prince ground the pebbles against the millstone, which made such a loud noise that the demon fled in fright.

Finally, on the last night the demon challenged the prince to a fight. Swiftly the prince climbed onto the roof and jumped onto the demon's shoulders, knocking him down. Then the prince cut off the demon's hands and feet and tied him to the side of a cliff for the rest of his life.

The demon confessed that it was he who had been harassing the king while he was building the castle, so the prince and princess were able to return home safely, and they lived happily ever after.

 21

THE MAGIC BOTTLES

Long, long ago there was a poor peasant called Gopal. He and his wife lived in a small hut at the end of their village. Their life was the simplest, for they had no money for rich food or expensive clothes.

One day they found that they had no money left at all to buy food. All they had was a cow. Very sadly Gopal's wife said, "We must sell our cow or starve. Take her to the market and try to get a good price for her."

Gopal set off on the road to the market. On the way he met a dwarf. Gopal had a kind heart; he thought he could do the dwarf a good turn. He offered to carry the little man on his back and save him the trouble of walking. The dwarf smiled at Gopal and thanked him. After he had been carried a short distance, the dwarf said, "Now put me down. Since you have made friends with me, I want you to tell me why you are going to the market."

"I am going there to sell my cow," replied Gopal. "My wife and I are very poor. We have no money left to buy food, so we must sell our cow."

"Give your cow to me," said the dwarf. "I shall give you something in exchange."

"What is it?" asked Gopal.

"A bottle," replied the dwarf.

"What!" exclaimed Gopal. "Do you expect me to exchange my cow for a bottle?"

"Ah," said the dwarf. "This is a magic bottle. If you place it on a table and say, 'Begin,' two little men will jump out and bring the choicest food in golden dishes. You will never again be hungry for a good meal."

So Gopal exchanged his cow for the bottle.

When Gopal returned home his wife asked him how much he got for the cow. "I exchanged it for a bottle," replied Gopal.

"You foolish man," shouted his angry wife. "Have you no sense? What are we to do with a bottle?"

"Wait," said Gopal. "Control your temper. This is a magic bottle."

He placed it on a table and said, "Begin." Immediately two little men jumped out of the bottle and covered the table with dishes of only choice food. The plates were of pure gold. Gopal's wife was very happy. "How wonderful," she said, and they sat down to the delicious meal. After this they were never in want of good food, and by selling the dishes they soon became very rich.

The neighbors wondered how Gopal and his wife made so much money. One man especially was determined to find out. He was very rich himself but he was jealous of Gopal. When he learned that the magic bottle was the cause of Gopal's wealth, he asked Gopal to bring it to his home. He and his wife wished to see what it did. Gopal was foolish enough to do

as the man asked. When he returned home he found that the bottle had lost its magic power. The rich man had stolen the magic bottle and had given him an ordinary one instead.

Gopal and his wife were very poor again. One day on his way to the market, Gopal met his friend the dwarf.

"What's the matter?" asked the dwarf. "You look very sad." Gopal told him what had happened.

"I shall give you another bottle," said the dwarf. "Go straight to the rich man's house, place the bottle on a table, and say, 'Begin.' "

Gopal did as he was told. As soon as he said, "Begin," two little men, each holding a stick, jumped out of the bottle and thrashed the rich man till he cried out for mercy.

"Stop beating me," begged the rich man. "I will give you back your bottle."

Gopal was very glad to get back his magic bottle. Off he marched back to his own house, proudly holding a magic bottle in each hand.

MOTHER'S DAY

ONCE upon a time, there was a poor woman who was blessed with a child every year. But it was a short-lived blessing. Her babies always died before the year ended. Because of these repeated misfortunes, her mother-in-law hated her and regarded her as a useless and accursed member of the family. So, when the next infant was born, both the newborn child and the unfortunate mother were driven out of the house. The poor castaway went crying into the forest with her baby clasped to her breast.

Suddenly there appeared in the depths of the jungle a shining goddess who asked her the cause of her sufferings. The woman poured forth her tale of grief. The goddess listened sympathetically and then commanded her to remain where she was until midnight, for that very night, at that very spot, a banquet was to be celebrated. No fewer than sixty-four *yoginees* with their heavenly attendants would participate in the forest festival. The woman was to lay her child at their feet and pray for a blessing. So saying, the goddess vanished.

All day long she waited as she had been told, in doubt, anxiety and hope — she had so little to lose, so much to gain.

As midnight approached, there was a rushing of the wind among the trees. The forest, black as pitch a minute before, now became brilliantly lighted by the heavenly beams surrounding the yoginees. These slender-waisted goddesses were playing together on the edge of the lotus-covered pool. The poor woman fell upon her face before them, sobbed out her story, and ended with a prayer. She knew well that a dreadful punishment may overtake the mortal who rashly dares to break in upon the leisure of the goddesses. But the yoginees were moved by compassion, and they blessed her and her child. "Go thou in peace," they said. "Have no fear for your child. For know that your love and faith have saved him. He shall live and be blessed; but you must worship the yoginees hereafter upon this last day of the month of Shravana."

And thus the curse was removed.

Since then, many mothers in Maharashtra State strictly observe this day in the month of Shravana as a fast until after the worship has been performed at nightfall and all the children of the house have taken their meals. They know that love and faith will help their children as surely as the yoginees have promised.

THE MILKMAN AND THE MONKEY

ONCE upon a time there lived a milkman. He used to get up very early in the morning to milk his cows. Then he would carry his half-filled milk cans down to the stream which ran close by. Very quietly, so that no one would hear him, the milkman would fill the cans to the top with water. Then off he would go to the town in the valley where he supplied milk to many of the people. In the evening the milkman would return to the stream. With a loud noise and clatter he would set to work washing his milk cans and getting them ready for the next day.

Close to the stream grew a tall tree in which a monkey made his home. Each day he watched the milkman at work. He noticed how quiet the milkman was in the morning and what a noise he made in the evening. The monkey began to wonder what it was all about and watched the milkman carefully for a month.

Then one evening the milkman came to the stream. He put his milk cans down on the ground. He did not set to work washing them as he usually did, but instead he sat down to rest under the tree. When he had made himself comfortable, he took a bundle of money out of his pocket and began to count it. He had two hundred *rupees* which he had earned by selling milk to the townsfolk.

In a flash the monkey was down the tree. He snatched the money from the milkman and swung himself up into the highest branches. The milkman begged for his money to be returned but the monkey took no notice. He divided the notes

into two equal piles and then he said, "Milkman, one hundred rupees is yours. The other hundred belongs to the stream. Take your money. The rest I am giving to its rightful owner."

Saying that, he threw the money into the stream and the water carried it far away. As for the milkman, he had learned his lesson.

ONE MORE CHILD

ONCE upon a time there was a lady who had lots of money. She was very very rich indeed. She had plenty of food, many beautiful clothes, and a very large house which was like a palace, but she had no children. She was very sad.

One day she asked a lady friend of hers what she could do to have one child at least, and her lady friend told her, "Go to that poor woman who lives at the end of your lane, for she has a dozen children and works hard to feed and clothe them. Her husband too works hard to earn enough morsels of food for the children and I often have heard her groan and moan about her poverty and lack of food for her children. Go to her," said the lady friend, "for she will surely give one child to you who are so rich and who could feed the child much better."

The rich lady considered this advice and after a while she said, "But do you really think she would give away her child?"

The lady friend replied, "Why not? Take her a bag of gold and I'm sure she will hand you the child."

31

The following day the rich lady took a bag of gold and happily drove to the poor woman's hut. The poor woman could hardly believe her eyes when she saw such a rich lady condescending to step in her door. Nevertheless, she smiled in humble respect and offered the rich lady a little low stool. The lady sat down and made herself comfortable as best she could.

The children, who were sprawled about the hut, huddled close to their mother and cried for food. The mother rose, brought the pot of rice soup, and served the children, not in plates, not even on leaves (she was too poor to have even these), but in little shallow pits, scooped in the clay floor and polished smooth. There were twelve polished shallow pits, the shape of bowls, six in a row. The children began to eat while the poor mother looked on. After the children had eaten every grain, they rose. Then the mother went up to each pit in turn, scooped up the rice water with her hands and lapped it up with aching hunger. After she had lapped up the water left in the twelfth pit, she raised her eyes to heaven and sighed aloud. "Oh, God! if you had but given me one more child, I would have had one pit more with which to satisfy my hunger."

The rich lady looked on in silence, amazed to hear that poor woman wishing for still one more child. Would she then part with one child for adoption? No, never! Thinking thus, the rich lady rose, pushed the bag of gold toward the poor woman, and left the hut, going her way a sadder but wiser woman.

THE CALM BRAHMAN

IN THE KINGDOM of a very great, good-natured and rich king, who was a patron of learning and wisdom, there lived a learned and pious Brahman youth. He was so honest and selfless that he would never go to anyone for help or money, certainly never to the king.

The king was very fond of inviting learned and wise men to his court and always gave them rich rewards and two handfuls of pearls. Many learned men came to the king's court to receive the rewards and the pearls. But though he had many invitations, the learned Brahman youth, whose name was Yatnakant, never went to the king's court. He strongly disliked riches. It pleased him to be learned, pious and poor.

The Brahman's wife was very annoyed by his attitude. She constantly criticized and quarreled with him for not acquiring riches. One day she pestered him so much that Yatnakant was forced to go to the king's palace. The king was highly pleased and greatly surprised to see him at court. He received the Brahman with much honor, offered him great riches and heaped

 33

pearls on him. But Yatnakant would not touch even a single *pie* (penny). "I cannot accept these riches," he said, "because they do not belong to the king. They belong to the king's subjects. But I will accept anything offered which is earned by the king's own labor."

The king, being a very good-natured man, was pleased with the suggestion, although all the courtiers were enraged at this insignificant Brahman's impudence and rudeness. In spite of their protests, the king went the very next morning to a poor man's farmyard to ask for a laborer's job. The farmer, not knowing the king, was extremely pleased to get a farmhand, but being very poor he only offered him four *annas* per day as wages. Though not much pleased, the king accepted the offer and worked hard the whole day. In the evening he received his daily wage and went home very proud, although he was exhausted and ached all over.

The next morning he invited Yatnakant to the court. When Yatnakant arrived, he could see that the king had really worked very hard. But when the king offered him the whole of his precious earnings, he would still not accept them, to the great surprise and slight annoyance of the king. "What do you want now?" the king demanded.

"May it please Your Majesty," said the Brahman, "I must do some service for you. Only then will I accept my wages." So saying he went to the king and nicely massaged his aching body, giving him much relief.

The king was pleased with the Brahman's honesty, straightforwardness and selflessness. When the massage was over, he made Yatnakant sit in a place of honor and again offered him his entire earnings. Still Yatnakant would not accept the four annas, to the annoyance of the king.

The king demanded an explanation. "O Lord of the Universe," the Brahman said, "the whole amount does not belong either to you or to me, for some share of it must go for the maintenance of your family. One part must go for you and one for your wife, one for your son and the rest I will accept."

The king was pleased with the Brahman's reasoning, and gave him only one anna, which he changed to two *pice*. After receiving them, Yatnakant went home, pleased to the sky.

The first time Yatnakant had gone to the king's palace his wife and children had expected him to bring home a great load of wealth. But he had come back empty-handed after dictating his strange conditions to the king. When the family saw he had returned penniless, they were enraged. They scolded him with harsh words and condemned him. Even so, he was very calm and quiet, and his peace of mind was not disturbed in the least.

When he went to the court the second time, naturally they had much higher expectations of him. When he again came home empty-handed, they were even more angry than before and created a terrific row. Still Yatnakant kept very cool and calm. He comforted them and told them he had not returned empty-handed this time, but had brought a precious gift, the value of which could not be measured in rupees and annas.

Naturally, they were eager and impatient to see the invaluable gift. So he proudly took out those two copper coins and handed them over to his wife. Alas, when the family saw those two coins they all shrieked in despair and disappointment. His wife in a great rage flung the two coins into the backyard.

Again, Yatnakant was not disturbed. After some time, finding it was useless to argue or quarrel with him or scold him, the family decided to leave him alone. They went about their daily chores, cursing their bad luck for having to be connected with him at all.

A few days later two strange-looking shoots sprouted out of the ground in the backyard. They grew into plants and then into wonderful trees. Everyone wondered and marveled at their beauty, splendor and strangeness. No one could make out what kind of trees they were. Thousands flocked to see them.

Lo and behold, one day those two trees made a strange noise and innumerable precious pearls started to shower from them. The family's joy knew no bounds. The whole town, including the king, came to see this marvelous sight.

Yet Yatnakant was neither disturbed nor overjoyed. In fact, he paid no attention at all to this remarkable event.

THE JACKAL AND THE CROCODILE

ONCE upon a time there lived in the jungle a jackal who was very cunning. He owed his life to his wits and alertness. In the same jungle there was a river and in this river lived a crocodile. The crocodile and the jackal were the greatest of enemies, and the crocodile had on many occasions tried to catch the jackal and eat him up. But the jackal had always managed to escape by his cunning.

One day the jackal, feeling thirsty, went down to the river to have a drink. As he was lapping up the cool water he thought he saw a log floating toward him. On closer examination he could make out two eyes and two nostrils. He drew back onto the bank, and to make sure that it was the crocodile trying to fool him, he spoke out loud. "Hey! Why is this piece of wood floating? If it is really a log of wood, then it should sink."

Hearing this the crocodile dived and went under. The jackal thanked his own alertness and ran off into the jungle.

Another day the crocodile, feeling very foolish for his slipup, decided to try to trap the jackal once again. He knew the jackal's favorite berry patch, so he crawled off to the patch and, covering himself with berries, lay perfectly still. Along came the jackal, but he stopped short as he saw all the berries piled up suspiciously into a long shape. He guessed at once that it was the crocodile hiding there waiting to catch him. To make certain, he called out, "O berry patch, why are you lying so still today? Formerly you used to roll about on seeing me."

As soon as he heard this the crocodile started rolling. All the berries fell off him and there he was, in full view. The jackal laughed and disappeared into the jungle. Feeling very foolish indeed the crocodile crept back to the river.

The next day, however, the crocodile had a new idea. He would hide himself in the jackal's own house when he was out and catch him when he returned. So he lumbered off and, at an appropriate moment, popped into the jackal's den. But just outside the den was a patch of wet ground where the crocodile had left claw marks.

When the jackal returned, his keen eyes spotted the claw marks. He realized that this time the crocodile was hiding in his very own house, but he quickly thought his way out of this problem. He called out loudly, "O house, why are you so quiet today? Why do you not welcome me home as usual?"

The crocodile fell for the trick again and said, "O jackal, welcome home!"

Meanwhile, the jackal set fire to the den and soon it went up in flames with the crocodile inside. From that time on the jackal lived happily ever after in the jungle.

THE CLEVER CHILDREN
AND THE KIND TAILOR

ONCE there were two children called Ramesh and Rita. Their father had once been a clever musician but now he was dead and their mother was very poor. One day there was a competition in their town. The mayor was to give a prize of a hundred *rupees* to the two children who sang the best song.

"Oh, Ramesh!" said Rita. "Shall we try to win the prize? We could sing that pretty song Father taught us."

"But how can we enter the competition?" Ramesh asked. "We have no nice clothes to wear."

Rita felt very sad. "We could go to Narayan the tailor," she replied. "Perhaps he will make us some clothes."

"How can he make us some clothes?" Ramesh asked. "We have no cloth and no money to give him."

"Still we can ask him," said Rita. "He is a very kind old man."

So they went to see the tailor. "Oh, Narayan," said Rita,

"there is a singing competition in the town and we want to enter it. But we have no nice clothes. Can you make some clothes for us?"

Old Narayan shook his head sadly. "I have no money to spend on clothes for other people," he said. "I would like to help you but where can we find the cloth?"

"It need not be made all of the same cloth," said Rita. "Could you take a little piece of each kind of cloth and make me a dress?"

"Perhaps I can. Perhaps I can," said the tailor. "I have plenty of little bits of cloth. They are too small to make anything. Nobody wants them, and they will only be thrown away. Perhaps if I join them all together I can make a dress for you and a coat and hat for Ramesh."

The tailor picked up some little pieces of white cloth and soon he was sewing them all together. As he sewed he sang:

A little piece of this, and a little piece of that,
And we'll soon have a very fine hat.

In twenty minutes he had made Ramesh a nice hat. Ramesh put it on his head and he was very proud of it.

"Now I will make you a dress, little Rita," said the tailor. He chose lots of small pieces of brightly colored cloth. Some pieces were blue, some were red, some were yellow and some were green. He joined all the pieces together and made a lovely dress for Rita. Rita was very pleased.

"It is the most beautiful dress in the world," she said happily. "Thank you very much, Narayan."

"Now," said Narayan, "we must make a coat for Ramesh," and he sang:

A little piece of this, and a piece of the other,
And soon we'll have a coat for your brother.

Ramesh's coat was quickly finished. It was brown and red and gold. "I look as grand as a king in this coat," said Ramesh. "Thank you very much, Narayan."

"Now run home and practice your song," said Narayan. "Tomorrow is the day of the competition. I hope you win."

Rita and Ramesh went back home. All that day they practiced their song. Soon they could sing it beautifully.

The competition was at ten o'clock the next morning. Ramesh and Rita put on their fine new clothes and went to the mayor's house. Many children were waiting there, all wearing very nice clothes, but nobody had a coat and dress as nice as Ramesh's and Rita's. The mayor came into the room and the competition began. All the children sang very nicely, but nobody sang as sweetly as Ramesh and Rita.

"Ramesh and Rita sang the best," said the mayor, and he gave them the prize of a hundred rupees.

Ramesh and Rita said, "Thank you very much, sir," and they took the money home to their mother. She was very surprised because they had not told her about the competition.

"What clever children you are," she said. "And where did you get those pretty clothes?"

The children told her that old Narayan had made the clothes from small pieces of cloth. "That was very kind of him," said their mother. "And now that you have won the prize you must give Narayan ten rupees to pay him for his trouble."

So the children took ten rupees and gave it to Narayan. He was very pleased. "What clever children you are," he said.

"You are clever, too," said Ramesh. "You made us such nice clothes from small pieces of cloth. We could not have entered the competition if you had not made a fine coat and hat for me and a beautiful dress for Rita. We could certainly not have gone to the mayor's house in our old clothes."

Old Narayan smiled. "I don't really think the mayor would have minded," he said. "But thank you for the ten rupees. The money will be very useful." And Narayan smiled happily to himself, thinking what good, kind children Ramesh and Rita were.

THE LITTLE BIRD'S RICE

THERE ONCE was a mountain bird who had several children. Every day she would collect whatever food she could find, and in the evening when the sun began to set, she would fly back home to her nest where her little ones would be anxiously awaiting her.

One day while she was sitting on a wooden post which a carpenter used to support the logs he sawed, the grain of rice held in her beak suddenly fell into a crevice. She was very upset by the loss of this food for her children, and made many attempts to recover it, but in vain.

The bird thought and thought, and at last decided to go and ask the carpenter for help. She went to him and asked him if he would get the grain for her, but he refused. She, however, was not discouraged. She went to the king, addressing him thus: "O King, may it please Your Majesty to order the carpenter to saw out the post into which my grain has fallen so that I can recover it and fly back home to feed my hungry little children?"

"Get out of here, you saucy bird!" blustered the king.

But she did not lose heart. The image of her little ones anxiously waiting strengthened her against all obstacles in recovering the rice. She thought, "The queen may listen and feel pity for me."

So she went to the queen and begged her to persuade the king to order the carpenter to saw the post out and redeem the grain for her. The queen, too, turned her out. Then she went to the serpent who lived nearby and begged him to have pity on her and to go and bite the queen, for she had not heeded her prayer. The serpent said no and scrambled back into his hole. Then she turned to a *lathi* (wooden stick) that happened to lie there and told it all about her misfortune, pleading with it to beat the serpent to death. The lathi refused her too!

Next she went to the fire to have the stick burned and, being refused there too, to the water to have the fire quenched, but it also refused. She now went to the elephant and implored him to help her by drinking up all the water. She complained that the water had grown very arrogant and had insulted her. But the elephant scornfully bade her to go away. Thereupon she went to the net and begged it to ensnare the elephant. The net, at the mention of the elephant, drew back timidly, but as soon as the bird got up to go, it sprang up to catch her. Luckily she escaped unhurt.

The little bird by now was heartbroken, with neither the courage nor the strength to proceed any further. Sad and dejected she perched on a tree and broke into tears. She had lost all hope of recovering the grain.

Chinkoo the mouse saw her plight. After watching her crying and complaining for some time, he could not contain himself

any longer. Coming near her he gently inquired, "Sister, why do you weep so much? Can I help you?"

At first she was nervous and suspected him of some trick. But finding him in earnest, she opened her heart to him. She related the entire chain of events right from the carpenter's stubbornness down to the net's trickery and cruelty. Chinkoo became very indignant, particularly at the net. He cried, "Sister, keep your courage up! I will see if this rascal will not behave itself."

They went to the net and Chinkoo called aloud, "Hello, son. How do you do?" This was strange behavior, and the net could feel Chinkoo's fury beneath it. The net began to tremble with fear. It begged Chinkoo to spare its life and agreed to honor the bird's request.

Now all three, the bird, Chinkoo and the net, proceeded together to find the elephant. Seeing the net coming towards him
menacingly, the elephant at once understood what was hap-
pening and joined them without their asking. They now went
to the water tank. The sight of the elephant's trunk chilled the
water's heart. It could only do what the little bird had asked,
so they all started towards the fire.

As the procession proceeded along the road to the king's
palace, the fire, the lathi, and the serpent, each in turn, also
joined, until they all finally reached the king's court. The king
was startled out of his wits by such a grand parade of birds, ani-
mals and elements headed by the little bird. When they saw the
king, the elephant trumpeted, the water roared, the lathi
menacingly began to sway to and fro, and the serpent hissed.

 47

The queen rushed out of her bedchamber, looked at the procession with wonder and hurriedly whispered something in the king's ear. The carpenter was immediately sent for and ordered to saw the post down and bring out the grain. The tiny grain was retrieved. Before all the court it was given back to the little bird. As she departed for home she sang:

> *My task has been done,*
> *The rice has been won,*
> *I must now return to my nest,*
> *To feed and put my weeping children to rest,*
> *It is time for them to sleep — to sleep.*

THE KING'S TRUE CHILDREN

MANY YEARS AGO there was a king who had no children to inherit his kingdom. He had married six queens in the hope of having a son, but no son was born. At last he married a young and beautiful princess, of whom the old queens grew very jealous. They became even more jealous when they learned that she was to have a child.

The king was a keen hunter and spent much time roaming the vast forests of his country. While he was away one day, the youngest queen gave birth to a son. But the six old queens took the child from his crib, put him into a basket and floated it down the river. In the baby's place they put a stone. When the king returned they told him that the young queen was a witch and that she had spirited away the child and put a stone in the crib. They demanded that she should be sent away from the palace. But the king loved her dearly, and seeing her grief, refused to punish her.

The basket carrying the baby drifted down the river until it came to the sea. There an old fisherman, who had toiled all day

without catching any fish, drew it into his net. He was amazed
to see the beautiful child inside. He took it home to his aged
wife. They had no children of their own and were overjoyed
that the god of the sea had at last given them a son. They re-
solved to bring him up as their own.

Later the young queen had a daughter and the wicked queens
again took the child away and replaced her with a stone. They
put the baby into a large water pot and floated it down the river.

The king could no longer ignore the warnings of his six wives
so he agreed that they should punish the mother as they wished.
To humiliate her they said that she should be forced to keep
the crows from settling in the palace gardens. As she ran about
the gardens they laughed and jeered at her from the windows.

The water pot with the little baby girl inside was carried
down the river by kind water fairies, and it was caught in the
net of the same fisherman who had found the basket. The old
fisher folk were very happy to be presented with a daughter
also. So beautiful were the children, so obedient and good, that
the simple couple believed they were gifts sent by the gods
themselves.

One day, when the boy had grown into a tall handsome lad,
he had a dream. In this dream he saw a *yogi* sitting in medita-
tion on the top of a mountain. The holy man spoke to him and
said that he must prepare for a pilgrimage to the source of a
sacred stream. The prince awoke and told his dream to his
foster parents. The fisherman was deeply disturbed for he
knew not only that the journey was dangerous, but that for
many years no pilgrim had returned from it. But remembering
the strange arrival of the children and believing that perhaps

a special destiny was in store for them, he sadly agreed that the boy should go.

Before leaving, the boy placed a bowl of milk on the floor. "Look at this every day," he said. "If it remains white I am safe. But if the milk changes color, know that I am in danger."

The boy traveled for days over rugged mountains and broad plains till at last he came to the top of a hill from which he could see the sacred stream winding along in its gorge far below. The saint of his dream was sitting under a tree. The holy man had been in an unbroken trance for twelve years, but when the boy approached he opened his eyes.

"What is it you wish?" the man said.

"I have come according to your instructions," replied the boy simply.

"For many years I have sat here," said the saint. "Formerly many people came to descend to the river, but when they failed to return no one dared make the pilgrimage any more. How then can a young inexperienced youth like you succeed where others have failed?"

"I do not know," the boy replied. "I have come because you asked me."

So the holy man provided the boy with a catamaran (boat) and two large water pots. "Descend through the narrow ravine," he said, as they looked down upon the river valley. "But while passing through it you must not look either to right or to left. If you look back at all, you will be lost. Remember," he said, "your success depends on your looking straight ahead until you reach the cave in which you will find the source of the sacred river."

So the boy set out. At last the catamaran passed into the

narrow gorge leading to the source of the river. On either side the walls of the ravine rose above him shutting out the light of day. He was not afraid of the darkness, but as he traveled further he heard low moaning sounds which steadily grew louder until they filled the darkness. All the demons seemed to be descending on him, shrieking and crying out until the hills rang with their clamor. Terrified, he shut his eyes and ears. Then he felt invisible hands plucking at his clothes. On a sudden impulse, he looked fearfully over his shoulder, and all was lost.

At home in the fisherman's cottage his foster parents gazed in horror as the milk turned blood red in color. Heartbroken, the young princess decided that she would go to the sacred river and bring back her brother. In vain the fisherman tried to prevent her. She plucked a flower and placed it in his hands, saying that if it faded and died they would know that she too was lost.

Over mountains and plains she went until she came upon the holy man sitting in sorrow on the mountaintop. She cast herself down at his feet and implored his help in finding her brother. So he provided her with a catamaran and two water pots and gave the same firm instructions to her.

She set off and soon the catamaran was moving between the walls of the gorge where all the powers of darkness awaited her. Soon they were upon her, around her. They shrieked and moaned and twitched her garments with urgent invisible hands. But she crouched down between her water pots, looking neither to the right nor to the left. At length the voices grew fainter and faded away into the darkness behind her.

The catamaran approached the cave in which the tiny spring

issued from the rock. She alighted and filled her water pots. Instantly the cave was brightened with a strange glow and a haunting chant filled the air. She saw the motionless forms of pilgrims on the floor of the cave and began to sprinkle them with the holy water. At the mouth of the cave she found her brother and they embraced with joy. The pilgrims, risen as though from a deep sleep, filled their jugs with the water and began the long pilgrimage back to the top of the mountain.

At the fisherman's cottage the old couple anxiously watched the flower each day, still fresh and alive.

Great was the amazement of all the people when they heard that the ancient spell of the river had been broken by a young girl and hundreds of pilgrims were returning.

Now the king heard of this young girl, daughter of a poor fisherman, and he went with his attendants and courtiers to pay homage to her. Heralds went before the king giving gifts of money and food to the poor. Thus it came about that the king sat on the sands beside the old fisherman and found in him a simple faith and wisdom which he himself lacked. The six old queens sat beside the king and behind them stood the youngest fanning the royal family. The fisherman began to tell of how he had found these two beautiful children who, he believed, were gifts from the gods to him and his wife. But the young queen, hearing the story, cast herself at the feet of the king, sobbing that the children were her very own, floated down the river by the jealous queens.

The six queens tried to drag her away. "Impertinent and shameless woman," they cried, "how dare you impose thus on His Majesty!"

But so genuine was her grief that the king commanded them

to stand back while he heard her story. At last the wickedness of the queens was clear to all. They were sent away from the court and forced to wander in the forests as punishment. The two children returned to the palace with the king and queen, and half of the kingdom was given to the faithful fisherman.

THE LENGTH OF LIFE

ON THE BANKS of a village pond grew a big banyan tree. The birds who built their nests in it gathered at dusk and they all sang before settling for the night. Large numbers of squirrels lived in the hovels of its trunk, chirping all day and cracking nuts and berries. The cows and buffaloes with their calves satisfied their thirst at noon and rested in the shade of the tree.

In the pond lived, among others, a fish, a frog and a tortoise, who were very close friends. Every day they used to swim to the corner in the shade of the tree and talk matters over. They talked of birds and beasts and men and many things.

One warm evening the three met as usual, and their talk turned to the question of which of them could live longest. Said the fish in its fishy way, "I and my kind are peace-loving, pacing the waters all our lives, and we live a full term of one hundred years."

"Pooh!" boasted the tortoise. "I have a stony shell to protect me and I carry it from my childhood. I could live for a thousand years resisting death and disaster."

But the frog remained silent. When his boastful companions demanded his statement, the frog croaked in a weak voice, "I am a miserable wretch. I do not know when I will be picked up by the skilled talons of the eagle that ogles me day and night from the treetop there. My life span is unpredictable."

Even as they were talking, a fisherman from the village slyly stole upon the scene and cast his net over the friendly group. When he dragged it forth he found the three of them huddled in one corner. He picked up the fish, ruthlessly hooked it by the nose and slipped it into his basket. He took out the tortoise, turned it, legs up, on a hard rock and placed a weighty stone upon it. But as for the wretch of a frog, he was let go and he gaily leaped back into the water. As he went he sang a wicked song heard by the tortoise:

> *A hundred years is hooked.*
> *A thousand years is booked.*
> *A shell below, a stone atop,*
> *But I go hopping, hop, hop, hop!*

THE CARTMAN'S STORIES

THERE ONCE was a very poor farmer who had such a small farm that it was only with great difficulty that he was able to care for his family with its earnings. Still, like most Indian farmers, he lived a happy and contented life. Men are usually self-satisfied and contented with their lot whatever it may be. But that is never true of women. The farmer's wife was always grumbling about her fate and cursed him for his poverty. She urged him to do some side business to add to the small earnings of the farm.

One day he finally got tired of his wife's pestering and decided to do something about it. He took out his cart and put it up for hire. Fortunately he got a customer very soon. The village merchant wanted to take some merchandise to a nearby village, so he engaged the poor farmer.

After loading the merchandise they both started for the next village. On the way the cartman began to be bored by the complete silence of the merchant. He said to the merchant, "Sir, why don't you talk? Do you know any stories or yarns?"

The merchant was not a talkative fellow. He disliked talk. So, to avoid talking, he told the cartman, "Look, I will give you a story, but I will charge you one *rupee* for each story I tell."

The cartman took it as a joke and said, "Come! Come! Let us hear some nice stories from you. Nobody charges for friendly and free talk." The merchant would not agree and the cartman would not keep quiet. He kept nagging the merchant to tell a story.

The merchant thought he would teach him a good lesson.

"All right," he said. "Listen to my story.

"Never refuse or disobey a request made by the village council.

"My story is over," he said. "Pay me my rupee."

The cartman still thought it was all a joke, so he insisted on having another story. The merchant said, "All right. Listen to my second story.

"Never tell a secret or a truth to a woman.

"My story is over, give me another rupee."

The cartman still took it as a joke and insisted on a nice long yarn that would really entertain him.

The merchant said, "Very well, listen to my third story.

"Never tell a falsehood in a law court.

"My story is over. Give me my third rupee."

Still the cartman took it as a joke and insisted on a really good story. But the merchant would not tell one. He knew the poor cartman had no money to pay, and he did not want to waste his breath for nothing. The fare agreed for the trip was only three rupees. The merchant thought to recover it from the cartman as his payment for the three stories. For a long time he kept on arguing with the cartman, but he would not tell him any more stories.

At last they came to their destination. The cartman unloaded the goods and demanded his fare. The merchant said, "Pay me my three rupees for my three stories and I will pay you your fare."

The cartman never expected the joke would be carried so far and so seriously. He was so disappointed and dejected that he did not know what to do. He had no money for food or fodder for his bullocks. And worst of all, what would he tell his wife when he went home? He felt like drowning himself in the river. Dejected, disappointed and weary, the poor cartman started homeward. His fellow cartmen jeered at him for his foolishness, but he listened quietly to all the jeering.

On the way they all came to a village. A destitute beggar had died suddenly, and the village council had met to make arrangements for the disposal of the body. They wanted a cart to carry the body to the cremation ground, but nobody would agree to do it. They disliked the idea of carrying a dead body.

When our cartman was approached, he thought for a moment and then readily agreed, for he was very badly in need of money. Besides, he remembered the merchant's advice in his first story: "Never refuse or disobey a request made by a village council." He decided to see how true it was, since he had paid such a high price for it.

The village council members loaded the dead body into the cart and paid him a rupee for the freight. They told him to take the body to the cremation ground, burn it, throw the ashes into the holy river and then go to his home. The cartman transported the body, put it on the funeral bier, set fire to it and sat down to watch the burning body. When it had completely burned, he went to collect the ashes. To his great surprise he found many tiny, hot bits of glittering gold among the ashes. The gold had been around the waist of the body, hidden under the clothes, left there unknown to anybody. He quickly collected them, put them in his pocket, threw the ashes in the river, and went back to his home in the dead of night.

Before he returned, his companions had already reported the whole story to his wife, so the wife was waiting to scold him. She greeted him with very harsh words, but somehow the poor man succeeded in consoling her. He gave her the rupee he had earned and she was satisfied for the moment. When everybody was asleep he quietly got up and buried the gold in a secret place.

For several days he did not do any work at all but spent his time idling. His wife became very angry, but he did not pay any attention. One day he quietly took out a part of the hidden gold, sold it in the market and bought clothes and provisions for himself and his family.

People were astonished and very curious about his sudden wealth. When they asked him about it, he would say, "God comes in my dreams and gives me money." They would not believe him and planned to force the secret from his wife. But the wife did not know anything either. She was just as curious as the others, and she finally asked her husband. He thought for a time and then remembered the merchant's second story: "Never tell a secret or truth to womenfolk." So he said, "Look, dear, I go into the jungle and drink *dhattura* juice. Then my hairs become gold and I pluck them and sell them."

Now everyone knows that dhattura juice is poisonous, but

all the people started to drink it just the same. They all became seriously ill from the poison and some died. Complaints went to the police about this mishap. An enquiry was held and the source was traced to the cartman, who was arrested and put before the court.

When the judge asked the man to explain himself, he thought for a moment and told the whole truth from beginning to end, for he remembered the merchant's third story: "Never tell a falsehood in the law court."

The magistrate was greatly amused by his story and acquitted him, for he was quite innocent. He said, "It served the people right, for they did a foolish thing without considering the effects of their thoughtless actions."

Then the farmer lived very happily ever after.

THE IMPUDENT LITTLE MOUSE

ONCE upon a time there was a little mouse. He was always running hither and thither in search of anything he could find. One day he found a small white square of silk in the tailor's shop and ran away with it to his hole. He thought it would make him a very fine little cap, but he didn't want a white cap. He wanted a prettier, gayer color. So off he went to the dyer and asked him to make it a beautiful purple. The dyer looked at it and laughed. "Off with you," he said. "Have I not got better things to do? I have forty costly *saris* waiting to be dyed every color of the rainbow and where shall I find the time to dye this little scrap?"

The mouse was furious. He stamped his foot and said, "Do it for me right now or else,

> *I will go to the court,*
> *I will call the police,*
> *You will get a good beating,*
> *And I shall watch the fun."*

At mention of the police the dyer was scared and said, "No, no, brother mouse. Don't do that. I will do it right now." And he dyed the scrap a beautiful deep purple.

The mouse was still not satisfied. He was an elegant mouse and wanted something grander. He thought his cap would look finer with flowers of gold thread embroidered on it.

So off he ran to the *zariwalla* (worker in gold and silver thread) and asked him to embroider the silk. The zariwalla looked at it and laughed. "Off with you," he said. "My eyes and back ache from bending over my work night and day. Do you think I have time to waste on your little scrap?"

The little mouse was furious. He stamped his foot and said, "Do it right now or else,

> *I will go to the court,*
> *I will call the police.*
> *You will get a good beating,*
> *And I shall watch the fun."*

The zariwalla was frightened at hearing the name of the police and he said, "Oh, no, brother mouse, don't do that. See how quickly I'll do your work." His fingers flew over the silk as he embroidered it.

Well pleased, the mouse ran to the tailor and asked him to make a cap that would fit properly. The tailor looked at him and laughed. "Off with you," he said. "Have I no work to be done that I should sit wasting my time over this little scrap?"

The mouse was furious. He stamped his foot and said, "Do it right now or else,

> *I will go to the court,*
> *I will call the police.*
> *You will get a good beating,*
> *And I shall watch the fun."*

The tailor shook with fear. He closed his hands and pleaded. "Dear brother mouse, don't call the police. I will stitch your cap this minute." When the cap was finished the mouse put it on and it fitted him perfectly. He felt very happy and went skipping down the road.

On the way he met a street performer with his drum and his monkey. The mouse felt like dancing because he had a new cap and so he asked the *madari* for his drum. The madari said, "Oh, oh, if you take away my drum, how will my monkey dance?"

Then the mouse was furious. He stamped his foot and said, "Give it to me at once or else,

> *I will go to the court,*
> *I will call the police.*
> *You will get a good beating,*
> *And I shall watch the fun."*

At that the frightened madari quickly handed over his drum. Thumping it vigorously the mouse jumped up and down singing loudly, "My cap is so fine, it is finer than the king's."

Now, who should hear him but a policeman. He walked up to the mouse and said, "How dare you say such things about the king? Come with me to the jail." He led the mouse away, locked him up and took away his cap. But was our mouse afraid?

Oh, no. From between the bars he sang out loudly so that all could hear him,

Our king is a beggar, he has no cap.
So he has taken away mine.

When word reached the king about this, he felt ashamed and ordered his soldiers to free the mouse and give him back his cap.

With the cap on his head the little mouse went marching down the street boldly chanting,

The king was afraid of me; he gave me back my cap.
The king was afraid of me; he gave me back my cap.

Then he ran to his hole, folded his cap, put it carefully in a corner, and being very tired by now, closed his eyes and went to sleep — just as you must do now my story is ended.

THE RICH MAN AND THE TAILOR

ONCE upon a time there lived a rich man. He needed a new cap so he went and bought a quarter of a yard of fine white cloth and took it to the village tailor.

"Tailor," he said, "will you make me a cap from this piece of cloth?"

"Oh, yes," replied the tailor, "I shall be delighted to do so."

The rich man thanked the tailor and stepped out into the street. Suddenly he was filled with doubts. The tailor had seemed so pleased about making the cap that the rich man felt sure the cloth would be enough for two caps. Quickly he returned to the tailor's shop.

"Tailor," he said, "you had better make two caps out of that cloth."

"Oh, yes," replied the tailor, "I shall be delighted to do so."

Once outside the shop the rich man was again filled with doubts. This time he was sure the cloth would be enough for three caps. So back he went to the tailor's shop and ordered three caps. The tailor's reply was the same as before: "I shall be delighted to do so."

The rich man continued to return to the tailor's shop until he had ordered ten caps to be made from his piece of cloth. "When will they be ready?" he asked.

"Tomorrow at noon," replied the tailor.

The rich man hurried away. Now he was sure that the tailor would not be able to steal any of his cloth.

The next day he rushed to the tailor's shop. "Are my caps ready yet?" he asked.

"Yes," said the tailor, "here they are." He held up his hands. On top of each finger was a tiny little cap!

And that is how the rich man got his ten caps — and he paid the tailor for them too!

THE TINY BIRD AND THE KING

ONCE there was a tiny tailorbird who made her nest in a small corner of the king's garden. This king was so rich that his men spread out heaps of gold and silver coins to dry in the sun when they looked damp. One evening when the men were gathering up the coins, they forgot to pick up one silver coin which had rolled away from the rest.

The tiny bird found the bright coin, picked it up and kept it in her nest. She said to herself, "Now I am as rich as the king, since I have the same coin as he has."

And every now and then she sang, "Whatever wealth the king has in his treasury, the tiny bird has also."

The king heard this from his court and asked his men what the bird was saying. The men respectfully joined their palms together and said, "The bird claims that she has the same coin as your majesty."

The king laughed and asked his men to find out what it was the bird had. When he heard that she had a silver coin, the king said, "Well, that must be one of my coins, so bring it back to me."

The men did this and the next morning the tiny bird sang, "The king is so poor that he must take away the tiny bird's property."

"That bird is a nasty one," remarked the king when this was repeated to him. "Go, return the coin to her nest." The men obeyed.

The next morning the bird sang with great gusto, "The king was afraid and returned the tiny bird's silver." The king heard this and was mightily angry. He asked his men to catch the bird and said he would eat her fried.

His men readily caught the bird and took her to the king. The king went to his seven queens and asked them to fry her in butter and serve her to him.

One queen took the bird and said, "What a darling!" Then another queen took her to have a look. Then another and another. During one such transfer the bird got loose and flew away.

The queens were terrified. What was to be done now? The king would be furious if he found out. Suddenly one queen saw a frog jumping about the courtyard. She grabbed it, asked the other queens to keep absolutely quiet, then dressed and fried the frog, and served it to the king. The king liked its taste very much and thought that he had now punished the bird for her insolence.

When he went back to his court the king heard the bird singing, "What fun, what fun, the king had a fried frog for his lunch." This made the king furious. He spat and washed his mouth repeatedly and wanted to vomit out the frog from his stomach. And he ordered that the noses of all the queens be cut off at once for insulting him like this.

This was immediately done, and the bird saw it and sang, "One tiny bird was enough to make seven queens lose their noses."

The king almost went mad. He ordered his men to catch the bird again. This time he would swallow it whole. This was actually done with the help of much water, and the king held his mouth tightly shut so that the bird could not slip out again. Everybody was relieved and said, "This will teach the bird a lesson."

Suddenly the king gave a big belch. Before the courtiers knew what had happened the bird flew out with the belch. "Catch her! Catch her!" cried the king. The guardsman grasped her and the same wonderful act was repeated. This time the king, after swallowing the bird, pressed his palms to his mouth to prevent her escape, and the guardsman stood by with an open sword to cut the bird to pieces if she flew out again.

But the bird struggled very hard in the king's stomach, and after a time the king belched again and the bird and all the water came out.

Everybody shouted, "Guard, guard! Kill her! Kill her!" The confused guard struck at the bird with his sword but missed her and instead cut off the king's nose. The king groaned loudly. The doctor was called in and after much trouble managed to bandage the wound.

The tiny bird sat on a branch and sang, "Look at the king with his nose off. He has been rightly served." Then she flew away and left the kingdom. The men found only her empty nest.

THE KID AND THE TIGER

A GOAT lived in a small cave on a hillock near a forest which adjoined some cultivated fields. She had a young kid who was still too young to be allowed far out of the cave. Whenever he wanted to go out, she would warn him, "Wild boars will get hold of you, or tigers will carry you away, or a lion will eat you up."

The kid would become frightened and remain quietly in the cave. When he got older, however, he became bolder, and as soon as his mother left the cave to get her food, he peeped out and gradually, bit by bit, strayed out further and further, until one day he roamed quite far away.

Soon he met a big ox munching tall grass. The kid had never seen such a big animal before and did not know what it was. But seeing that it had horns like his mother, he decided that it must be another goat who had grown big by feeding on better food than his mother could get. So he approached the ox and asked, "What do you eat, big animal?"

The ox said, "Why, I eat grass, of course!"

The kid said, "So does my mother but she is not so big as you."

The ox said, "But I eat much more and much better grass than your mother ever gets."

The kid asked, "And where do you get that?"

The ox said, "Why, in the forest."

The kid said, "You must take me there." So he followed the ox to the forest and found the grass excellent. He ate so much of it that he could not move at all.

At nightfall the ox said, "Let us return home now."

But the kid could not walk a step so he said, "You go back. I shall return tomorrow." The ox went away and the kid found a hole nearby and crawled in to rest and sleep.

That hole really belonged to a fox who had gone to a feast at the lair of his uncle, the tiger. When he returned late at

night he found that some other animal was occupying his hole. Because it was dark and the kid was black in color, the fox suspected that a giant might be in his hole. So he asked in a rather low voice, "Who is there?"

The kid was very clever and said, "I am Narahari Das, the uncle of a lion. I shake my long beard and can swallow fifty tigers in one gulp."

The fox was frightened and ran off as fast as he could. He did not stop until he reached the tiger's lair. The tiger was much surprised and asked, "Why, nephew, what makes you come back in such a hurry?"

The fox, breathing hard, said, "O uncle, I am in great danger. A Narahari Das has occupied my hole. He claims that he can swallow fifty tigers in a gulp."

The tiger was very angry and said, "Is that so? Did you actually hear him say that? I shall soon find out how he can do it."

The fox said, "But uncle, I dare not go back to him. If he finds me again and wants to swallow me, you would be off in two big jumps, but I cannot run as fast as you and he would surely finish me off."

The tiger said, "Don't you worry. I shall never desert you."

The fox said, "Very well, in that case, let us tie our tails together." The tiger did this and the fox felt assured that the tiger could not leave him in the lurch. So they reached the entrance to the fox's hole.

The kid saw them from a distance and shouted to the fox, "You idiot, I gave you the price of ten tigers and you have returned with only one, dragging him by the tail."

On hearing this, the tiger got the fright of his life. He thought that the fox must have deceived him and brought him to Narahari Das to be eaten. So he did not wait any longer but ran off in big bounds twenty-five feet long, with the fox tied to his tail. The poor fox got thrown roughly to the ground, had his skin torn by thorn trees, and was bumped repeatedly on the hard mud edges of the fields. "Uncle, stop!" he shouted. "We are falling on hard borders." But the tiger got more frightened and ran faster than ever, and this went on all through the night. In the morning the kid returned home. The fox was very angry with the tiger and could never forget his pain and humiliation.

THE COBBLER'S DEITY

ONCE in a village of cobblers there lived two cobbler women; one was the mother-in-law and the other the daughter-in-law. The mother-in-law was very domineering and hard-hearted. Under her watchful eye the daughter-in-law had to do all the work in the house. As a reward she used to get only scoldings and the remains of one meal a day.

One day she was given some wheat to grind on a grindstone. She was ordered to turn the handle of the grindstone with one hand and to ring a bell with the other so that she could not steal the flour and sell it while the mother-in-law was having her nap. All this misery only made the girl cunning and smart. She rang the bell with her toes while she stuffed many handfuls of flour into a bag under her *sari*. When the day's work was done and the people of the house were preparing for the night's rest, the daughter-in-law, hungry and restless, went out of the house. She took the bag of flour with her and went straight to the temple of their deity. At the feet of the god in the temple she found the offerings of butter and molasses. She thought,

"What a waste, so much is lying about which no one needs. If I take some to satisfy my hunger surely nobody will know."

Thus pacifying her conscience she took the *ghee* and molasses, mixed them with the flour, brought some wood, made a fire, and baked some sweet *chappaties*, which she ate with gusto. Seeing all this the deity, who was sitting on its pedestal with its hands on its thighs, put two forefingers into its mouth in amazement. After she had eaten, the daughter-in-law tidied the place, thanked the deity and went home to sleep.

The next morning was a holy festival. When the worshippers gathered at the temple they were shocked to see their deity with its fingers in its mouth. They tried their utmost by praying, fasting and offering valuable gifts to please the deity. But to no avail. They announced a reward in cash to anyone who could make the deity return to its original position. Practically everyone tried but failed!

Hearing all this, the daughter-in-law, who knew what was wrong with the deity, asked her mother-in-law for permission to try to bring the deity back to its former posture. All the people laughed and made jokes at the girl's proposal, but the worried head of the village accepted it and asked her to try. The daughter-in-law asked him to close all the doors of the temple and allow no one to come near it except herself. Then she entered alone and went to the deity and said, "People offer you many nice things, yet when a poor starving woman like me takes some of it you make such a fuss. After all, you are only a cobbler's deity. You need a thrashing with a slipper."

Thus saying, she took off her slipper. The deity immediately took the fingers out of its mouth and went back to its former position. When people saw this they were overjoyed, and praised and rewarded the daughter-in-law. Her mother-in-law was so awed by this incident that she stopped mistreating her daughter-in-law and took pride in her. The girl went to the deity and thanked it for bringing her good luck and happiness.

THE BRAVE LITTLE PRINCE

ONE DAY a certain king, who was very keen on shooting, saw a beautiful woman abandoned under a tree in the forest. He fell in love with her, took her back to his palace, and made her his seventh wife. But she was a witch in disguise and was soon able to persuade the king to get rid of his six other wives. This he did by casting them in a dungeon under the earth after first putting out their eyes. Each day food was let down an abandoned dry well to the six queens.

The youngest of the queens gave birth to a son who grew into a handsome, clever little fellow. He was able to find his way out of the dungeon by underground tunnels and bring back useful things for the six queens.

One day the king saw him wandering around the palace gardens and took an instant liking to him. He decided to adopt the little boy. But the enchantress queen was very jealous and wanted to kill him.

One day the queen called him to her and said, "I want you to take a message to my mother, who lives alone in the mountains. Take this letter and give it to her." After informing the six women in the dungeon of his trip and assuring them that he would be back the next day, the boy set out fearlessly.

Night fell before he could reach his destination and he asked for food and a place to sleep at an old couple's cottage near the forest. The old man liked the young lad, but he was curious about his mission, for he knew that the woman who dwelt in the mountains was a notorious witch. So he opened the boy's wallet while he slept and read the letter. The queen had instructed her mother to kill the bearer of the note as soon as she received it. The old man angrily replaced this wicked letter with another in which he instructed the witch to feed and tend to every desire and need of the letter-carrier as soon as he arrived.

The unsuspecting boy arrived at the castle of the witch the next morning and delivered the substitute letter. He was extremely interested in the many flasks and bottles of colored mixtures in the witch's den and asked her all about her magic. She showed him a black box in which, she said, were six pairs of eyes belonging to six queens. She also showed him magic flasks that could be used to make thorns, fire, mist, and water spring up suddenly.

The boy then asked for a drink of water, but he said, "I can drink only water which has been drawn up in a sieve."

So the old woman tried to draw up water in a sieve but of course she was not able to do so. While she was busy at the well, the boy snatched up the black box and the four magic flasks and sped down the mountain.

The witch chased him, but when he saw she was gaining on him he threw up a hedge of thorns around her from the first

flask. She fought her way through and again caught up with him. He threw the flask of fire and then the flask of water, but she crossed through both. But when he conjured up a thick mist from the fourth flask, she lost track of him and he was able to get away safely.

He took the black box with the six pairs of eyes back to the queens in the dungeon and then went to the king and told his story. The wicked queen was driven out of the kingdom. The king took back his six queens and they all lived happily.

≫

THE GOLDEN SKINS

≫

A CERTAIN MAN had seven sons, six quite normal and one
an idiot — at least that is what his brothers thought him to be.
He could not speak properly and the people of the village
called him a Lātā.

When the father died the six sons were given handsome por-
tions of the property, but the Lātā was given a thin and sickly
bull-calf. Every morning when he let it loose, it grazed down
his brothers' crops until in desperation they killed it.

The Lātā wept bitterly. "At least give me the skin," he
moaned. So he took the skin, cleaned and pegged it, and when
it was dry set off for the nearest town to sell it. Night fell
while he was still in the forest so he climbed up a tree for
safety.

Later in the night a marriage party happened to camp under
that very tree. The Lātā found that squeezing the skin caused
it to squeak loudly. The terrified people below thought that
there was a demon in the tree and they fled, leaving behind all
their baggage. The Lātā climbed down, collected all the money
and jewelry he could find, and went home.

Early in the morning he went to the house of one of his sisters-in-law and asked for a corn measure. Curious to know what it was that he wished to measure, she put some honey in the bottom. When the Lātā returned the measure she found a small gold earring stuck to the bottom. His six brothers then wanted to know where he had got so much wealth that he had to measure it.

"I sold the skin of my bull," the Lātā replied.

"But for *so* much?" they cried incredulously.

"Yes," he said seriously, "skins are fetching good prices at the next town. It's a long walk but it is worth going the distance."

So the six brothers killed all their cattle and set off. "Skins for sale! Skins for sale!" they cried. "A bushel of gold pieces for one." The people not only laughed at their stupidity but took them for madmen and chased them out of their town. Realizing that they had been fooled they went home and burned down the hut of the Lātā.

"At least let me have the ashes," he moaned. So he took half a sack of gold, filled it to the top with the ashes, and set off. On the way he had to cross a swift-flowing river. The Lātā was strong and unafraid, but a wedding party stood on the bank wondering how to get across. The Lātā offered to carry the more timid ones across on his back if the others promised not to touch his sack of gold, otherwise it would all turn to ashes.

When he had carried the men over, he opened his sack and, of course, found it half full of ashes, just as he had left it. But he accused the men and said, "You touched my sack. You touched my sack. See how half the gold has turned into ashes." The marriage party, already being much delayed, and afraid that the local villagers would come out and quarrel with them, offered him some money. But this was not enough. "Replace all the gold that has become ashes," the Lātā demanded. So they filled his sack to the top with gold and left.

The Lātā, well satisfied, returned home and sat down under a tree in the courtyard of his brothers' house. Again he asked one of his sisters-in-law for a corn measure. She also put honey in the bottom and when he returned it, she found a gold coin stuck there.

The Lātā's six brothers were determined not to be fooled a second time, so they took away all his gold and put him into a sack. This they placed at the very edge of the river, hoping that if he struggled to get out, it would topple into the water and he would be drowned.

As he sat inside the sack the Lātā poked a tiny hole in the side. Through this hole he saw riding down the road a prince on a beautiful white horse. To attract his attention the Lātā began to sing. He sang of all the fine things that he could see from inside the sack, all the wonders visible from the edge of the river in the depths below. The prince stopped in astonishment.

"Of course you are amazed," said the Lātā. "But you would be even more surprised if you could see what I see."

Now the prince was on his way to claim the hand of the king's daughter, but he was in no hurry. So he opened the sack and let out the Lātā. He then took off his crown, cloak, and fine tunic and climbed into the bag. The Lātā tied up its mouth tightly and when the prince struggled he toppled into the river and was drowned.

After dressing himself in the prince's fine clothes, the Lātā mounted the prince's horse and rode homeward. "As I sat by the water," he told them, "our mother came up in the form of a frog and she took me down to the bottom of the river. There I met the king of the river and he gave me these fine clothes and this horse."

The six brothers then demanded that he should place each of them in a sack and put them at the edge of the river. This he very readily did. They waited and waited in vain for their mother to come up and invite them down. When she did not come they each toppled their sacks into the water themselves and were drowned. The Lātā rode off toward the king's palace dressed as a prince. When he showed his gold and jewels, and the extent of his property, the king agreed to give his daughter to him, and he lived happily ever after.

THE PANDITJI AND THE GUAVAS

ONCE upon a time there lived a Panditji. He was a very devout man. Every morning before dawn, winter or summer, he used to go to the river to have his morning dip and to say prayers. Now this Panditji was very fond of guavas. On his way to the river he had to pass through a guava grove. Each time he passed under the trees he noticed them as they first bore flowers and then the fruit.

In the cold and frosty month of December he watched the guavas grow bigger and more luscious day by day. One by one they began to ripen and his mouth watered each time he looked at them.

A gardener tended the grove, but in such bitter cold and so early in the morning he usually sat wrapped up in a blanket inside his hut. So it seemed to the Panditji that the grove was deserted.

One morning, on his way back from the river, the Panditji could hold himself no longer and he gave in to his temptation. But to appease his conscience he said to himself, "I will not steal

these guavas, I will ask the tree itself whether I can take them or not."

Then he spoke out loud, "O tree of the most delicious guavas, may I pluck four or five of your fruit?"

And answering his own question, he said, "Why not, O wise Panditji? You may take forty or fifty."

Thus saying, he climbed up the tree and carefully picked off about fifty of the ripest and sweetest fruit. Then he put them all in his cloth bag, clambered down, and went on his way. The fruit was as delicious inside as its golden appearance promised.

The next day he followed the same routine and cleaned off another tree. Daily he carried on this procedure.

After some time the gardener began to notice the missing fruit. All the trees without fruit seemed to be along the foot-path which went through the grove. He became angry that anyone should take the fruit from his grove without even asking his consent. Wrapping himself in blankets against the cold, he sat down on his cot behind a tree with the footpath in full view. He stayed up the whole night, shivering in the icy wind, thinking about the dire punishment he would inflict on the culprit.

Just as dawn was breaking, in the first glimmer of light, he spied a figure coming down the path. It was the Panditji. But he walked straight on. The gardener thought that his night-long vigil had gone to waste and was preparing to leave when he saw the Panditji returning. This time he was walking slowly and looking up into the trees. On the spur of the moment the gardener drew himself behind a tree and watched. The Panditji chose a well-laden tree and carried out his conversation as before: "O tree of the most delicious guavas, may I pluck four or five of your fruit?" And answering his own question he said, "Why not, O wise Panditji? You may take forty or fifty."

As he started to climb the tree, the gardener dashed out and caught hold of him. The Panditji nearly jumped out of his skin, but regained his composure and scolded the gardener for frightening him. "What is the matter with you, my good man? Why are you gripping my hand so hard? Let me go. I am late."

The gardener choked down his anger and said, "I have seen with my own eyes and heard with my own ears what you were going to do. And you are the same person who robbed these other trees of their fruit. Now you come with me and I'll show you what I do to people who steal my guavas."

The Panditji realized that his trick had been found out and started to whimper. "O gardener, have pity on me. Please pardon me this time. I will never do it again. After all, I asked the permission of the tree before plucking."

But the gardener held him fast and dragged his plump form to a nearby well. There he first tied the Panditji's hands and then attached a big basket to the well-rope. The Panditji watched these proceedings with growing alarm, appealing for forgiveness. But the gardener would have none of it. He pushed the Panditji into the basket and lowered it some distance into the well. "O well which gives my guava trees water, may I give Panditji a plunge in your water?"

The Panditji yelled out in anguish at the prospect of a plunge in the icy water and begged for forgiveness once again. But the gardener answered himself, "O industrious gardener, why just a plunge? Give him forty or fifty."

So saying, he lowered the Panditji into the water. The cold water took all the Panditji's breath away. Then he was drawn up, shivering and with teeth chattering. He could hardly speak. He was lowered a second time. He turned nearly blue with the cold and could not utter a word. Only his eyes appealed for pity.

The gardener drew him up, released his hands, and telling him to go, forbade him even to look at the trees again. The Panditji could only stutter his thanks, but he made up his mind never to touch another guava.

THE MOON PRINCESS

DID YOU KNOW that a beautiful princess lives in the moon? She lives with her old, old grandfather. This is the story of how they got there.

Many, many years ago in India there was a beautiful princess. Her name was Radha. All the princes in the country wanted to marry Radha because she was as sweet as she was beautiful. But she did not love any of them, and she did not wish to marry. "I don't like any of the young men," Radha told her grandfather. "Ramesh is handsome, but he is not as handsome as he says he is. Prakash is rich but never gives any money to the poor. Gopal is fat and always hungry. And Ganesh is thin, but he too is always hungry. I won't marry a man who talks about food all the time."

Radha's grandfather laughed. "You'll never marry, my child. You will find in this world that you cannot have everything in a man."

Radha looked out of the window. It was ten o'clock at night and the full moon shone on the pool at the bottom of the garden, making a little path of silver on the water. "There are other worlds," she said, looking at the moon. "I want to marry someone as beautiful as the moon."

All at once she saw that the silver path from the pool stretched right up to the moon, and there was a little man running down the path.

"Look, Grandfather," she cried. "A little man has jumped out of the moon and he's running down the moonbeam to the pool."

"Don't be foolish, my child," said her grandfather. His eyes were old and he could see nothing unusual.

"It is true," Radha said.

The little man had reached the pool now, but he did not look into the water. He ran on the moonbeam until he came to Radha's window and then he stopped. He looked at her, and she looked at him. The old grandfather was able to see him now, too, and what a strange little man he was. He was yellow all over: yellow hair, little yellow face, yellow clothes, and the yellow glowed like a light. He made a little pool of light in the darkness outside the window. His eyes twinkled like stars.

"Good evening, Princess Radha," he said at last. "Prince Moon told me to come to you. He says you want to marry him."

"Prince Moon?" said Radha. "Who is Prince Moon?"

"He is the handsomest, the richest, and the kindest of all men," said the little yellow man.

"Is he kind to the poor?" asked Radha.

"He gives half of his money to the poor every year," said the strange little man.

"Does he eat a lot of food?" asked Radha.

"He eats twice a day, but only a little," answered the little yellow man.

"Does he know that he is handsome?" continued Radha.

"No."

"Oh!" said Radha, "I might like him, then. But why did he tell you to come here?"

Her old grandfather, who had been listening open-mouthed, said, "Where have you come from? How did you get here?"

"I've come from the moon," replied the little yellow man.

"Yes, I saw him," Radha said. "I told you, Grandfather."

"You told me," said the grandfather, getting angry. "You told me, you foolish girl. How can anyone come all the way from the moon?"

"I can," said the little yellow man. He, too, was getting

angry. "I can, and I did. You're a foolish old man with blind old eyes, and so you didn't see me coming. But Princess Radha saw me."

"She thought she saw you," said the grandfather, "but she didn't. How could she? No one can visit us all the way from the moon."

"I can and I did," said the little man again. He was very angry now and his yellow face was turning quite dark and red.

The grandfather started to laugh. "Go back to your beautiful moon, then," he said. "I should like to see you do it."

"I will but I'll take you with me," shouted the little yellow man. "I'll teach you to laugh at me." He caught the old grandfather by the front of his coat and pulled him out of the window.

"Help! Help!" shouted the grandfather, as he felt himself being carried toward the moon. "Save me, Radha, save me."

Radha caught her grandfather's feet and pulled. But the little yellow man pulled harder and away they went through the dark night sky, up, up, up toward the moon. And that was the last time they were ever seen in this world.

All the princes — the handsome and rich ones, the fat ones and thin ones — married other princesses. No one remembers the beautiful Princess Radha now. But she is quite happy. She is married to Prince Moon, and he is as handsome and as kind and as rich as the little man said he was, and he never talks about food.

The old grandfather is happy too. He quarrels every day with the little shining yellow man and it makes him laugh because he likes a good quarrel. But the yellow man often gets very angry, and his shining yellow face turns red and dark, and he shuts himself up in his house.

That is why the moon does not shine all through the month. But when it is full and shining you can look up and see the old grandfather sitting there, laughing and laughing to himself.

WORD MEANINGS

Anna: An anna is a small unit of Indian money. Formerly sixteen annas were equal to one rupee. A rupee is worth about fifteen cents.

Brahman: There traditionally are four classes in India. Roughly these are priests or teachers, soldiers, merchants, and servants. The brahmans, or priests and teachers, are the highest class in Hindu society. They are generally revered as holy and learned men, though, of course, there are exceptions.

Chappaties: A chappatie is an Indian form of bread that looks somewhat like a pancake or a tortilla. It is made of wheat and forms a daily part of the meal, particularly in North India.

Conjee water: The water in which rice has been boiled. It is sometimes used as a diet for people who are ill.

Cooly: A name generally given to hired laborers and burden carriers throughout India. It is sometimes also used to indicate common men of the lower classes.

Cowrie: A small shell widely found in the Indian Ocean. In early times it was sometimes used as money in India.

Word Meanings

Dhattura: An Indian plant used to stupefy and poison. It is also sometimes used as a narcotic.

Ghee: Clarified butter which looks somewhat like cooking oil, long used in India as an offering to the gods as well as in cooking and as lamp fuel.

Guava: A round tropical fruit about the size of an orange. It is very sweet and much liked by Indians. Guavas from Allahabad in India are especially delicious and well liked.

Lātā: An offensive name sometimes applied to persons who babble without speaking any understandable words. It is also a mental disease of a special type of nervous condition.

Lathi: A long, heavy, wooden stick sometimes used as a weapon or policeman's club.

Madari: A street performer who earns money by performing tricks, often with a monkey, for passersby.

Maharajah: An Indian title meaning "great king."

Pandit (ji): A pandit is a learned Hindu who knows the ancient Indian language of Sanskrit as well as philosophy and religion. Often pandits are teachers or priests. The ending "ji" is a sign of respect given to any important person.

Patel: The head man of a village.

Pie (pice): A pie is the smallest unit of Indian money. Nowadays one hundred pice make one rupee worth about fifteen cents.

Rupee: The ordinary unit of Indian money, like the dollar in America or the pound in England.

Sadhu: A sadhu is a very holy man who has much wisdom and knowledge. He is a very respected saint in India.

Sari: Most Indian women wear a sari, which is a piece of cloth about six yards long wrapped around them in a very attractive manner.

Shravana: There are several different calendars in the world. In one of the Indian calendars the month of July/August is known as Shravana.

Yogi: A yogi is a very holy man who has through much discipline and religious knowledge gained a special understanding of the world.

Yoginee: There are many gods and goddesses in Indian religion. They all represent different parts of the real unity to which everything belongs. The yoginee is a special type of goddess.

Zariwalla: Indian cloth and garments are sometimes embroidered with gold and silver threads. This is very difficult work and it is done by a special class of people known as zariwallas.